an extract from
alexander trocchi's
young adam
with an enthusiast's view
by gillian mackay

an extract from
alexander trocchi's
young adam
with an enthusiast's view
by gillian mackay

Scottish **Book** Trust

2003

Published by
Scottish Book Trust
Scottish Book Centre
137 Dundee Street
Edinburgh EH11 1BG

Tel: 0131 229 3663

**From April 2003 Scottish Book Trust will be moving its offices
to Sandeman House, 55 High Street, Edinburgh EH1 1SR.**

ISBN: 1 901077 12 8
Copyright © Scottish Book Trust, 2003

Published with the support of the Scottish Arts Council National
Lottery Fund and The Hugh Fraser Foundation.

Young Adam is published by Rebel Inc.
an imprint of Canongate Books, ISBN: 0 86241 905 0

Extract copyright © Alexander Trocchi, 1954

Series design by Caleb Rutherford   eidetic
Printed in the UK by Cox & Wyman, Reading, Berkshire

contents

read **around books**

There is no shortage of fiction on the shelves of our bookshops – quite the opposite – but finding one that shouts out 'this is what you are looking for' is getting harder and harder as the number of books published goes up with each passing year. Too often we open a new book with expectation and enthusiasm only to discover disappointment and to struggle to get beyond page thirty. When we do find a book we really enjoy the urge is there to tell friends, colleagues and family to read it too in the hope that they will share our delight.

Read Around Books goes one step further and puts that enthusiasm down in black and white in the hope that many more readers will discover the joys of reading the very finest fiction that has emerged from Scotland over the last one hundred years. **This is a chance to sample before you borrow or buy.** Others have found these books before you, the writing held them spellbound and even when finished, these books would not let their readers go.

Each of the first twelve of these highly collectable little guide books promotes a work of fiction by a writer who lives in Scotland, was born in Scotland or who has been influenced by Scotland (our definition of Scottish is generous). Together they offer a marvellous introduction to the very best of Scottish writing from the twentieth and the first few years of the twenty-first centuries.

In each you will find a substantial extract, the enthusiast's view of the book, starting points for discussion for readers' groups, a short biographical piece about the author, and suggestions for similar reads which act as a further gateway to fine fiction.

Jan Rutherford
Series editor, 2003

the enthusiast

Gillian Mackay

Gillian Mackay is Press Officer in the publicity department at Faber and Faber. Previous to that she worked in bookselling for nine years, latterly as Events Manager at Borders in Glasgow, during which time she set up a broad programme of events including a variety of reading groups.

the enthusiast's **view**

Young Adam
by Alexander Trocchi

'*Young Adam* is a very fine novel. Rebel Inc. is to be congratulated on publishing what the author considered to be the novel's definitive version.'
– Ron Butlin, *Scotsman*

To paraphrase from the 1998 film, 'The Opposite of Sex', the central character in *Young Adam* doesn't have a heart of gold and doesn't intend to grow one. The same could have been said of the author in his lifetime. You don't have to spend long reading about the life of Alexander Trocchi before you come across the infamous stories of how he abandoned his children and pimped his wife to feed his life-long heroin addiction.

Through the novel *Young Adam*, an intense, subversive world is revealed to the reader. With such a notorious life story, Trocchi was ideally placed to give an insight into the mind of a character who challenges the reader's moral view. He channels a compelling thriller through the selfish, deceitful psyche of the promiscuous narrator, Joe, with chilling results.

First published in Paris in 1954 by the notorious Olympia Press, for whom Trocchi had been writing pornography, *Young Adam* is a novel in three parts. The story begins after one killing and ends just before another.

A young woman's body is found in the Forth and Clyde canal by two bargemen. The novel is narrated by one of the bargemen, a young drifter called Joe. Between reporting the discovery of the corpse and its removal by ambulancemen just after breakfast, Joe has developed a passion for his colleague's wife, Ella.

As they head off to deliver a load of anthracite from Glasgow to Edinburgh, the reader becomes drawn into the claustrophobic world of the barge through the mind of one of the most disturbed and compelling characters in twentieth century Scottish literature. And as the journey gets underway, it becomes clear that Joe knows more about the mysterious death of the girl found in the canal than he has admitted.

Life on the barge is physically intimate: Joe and his colleague, Leslie, work, wash, eat and drink together. On the barge, Leslie and Ella can hide nothing from Joe:

> 'And with only a wooden partition between them and me I knew quite a lot about them. I knew for example that Leslie was impotent.'

Despite living in such close proximity to one another, Joe's emotional connection with Leslie is minimal:

'It was as though, because we had nothing to say to each other, we had agreed to feign interest in the same thing... simply because to admit openly that no point of contact exists is to imply the superfluity of the other, and thus to undermine his very existence.'

The cool detachment with which he describes the discovery of the young woman's body at the beginning of the novel is extended to include all his human contacts. He provides incredibly detailed yet dispassionate descriptions of what he observes of the lives of the people around him. For example, when Joe meets Ella's sister, Gwendoline, he takes the opportunity to build a picture of her from what he sees and feels around her untidy flat in Leith:

'I glanced at the cigarette butts and the soiled underclothing pushed hurriedly out of sight under a cushion, and then I walked over to the bed again and put my hand on the sheet where she had lain. It was still warm and there was a feel of biscuit crumbs under my fingers. On the bedside table was a bent hairpin, a piece of ribbon, an ashtray with red-tipped fag-ends, and a little grey ball of chewing gum. Lying beside the ashtray was a bottle of aspirin. Like an inventory clerk, I took stock.'

However, although he may note the smallest detail about some of the other adults in the novel, he rarely mentions Ella and Leslie's son, Jim, who also lives within the tight physical confines of the barge.

There are other elements of Joe's story that may make the reader question his reliability. How much can the reader trust Joe as a narrator? How much should the reader believe the details of his story? How much of Joe's story is set up to justify his unwillingness to take responsibility or face the consequences of his actions?

He is untruthful to other characters throughout the novel. He lies to Leslie as soon as he tries to begin an affair with his wife with no other explanation than it seems to fill a vacuum of boredom he feels in a day that he has discovered a corpse:

> 'I pointed [the ambulancemen] to where we had put the body under the sacks. I left them to it. I was thinking again of the dead woman and . . . I was bored by the fact that it was the beginning of the day and not the end of it, days being each the same as the other as they were then, alike as beads on a string . . . '

This indifference would be shocking in any character but Joe's detachment becomes all the more extraordinary as the story develops.

He does not correct Ella in her assertion that they will marry in the future but claims to be 'temporarily unable to make any decisions'. He also justifies his deception of characters he meets later in the story, including Connie's husband and Daniel Goon. Furthermore, he tells us that he lived with his lover, Cathie, for two years and had known her 'for a long time', yet chose to give her a false surname:

'. . . I never told Cathie my real name. She knew me as Joe Taylor. I always gave my correct Christian name because it's difficult to remember and react normally to an incorrect one.'

There is something of the ridiculous about this, like in the 1973 film, 'Badlands', in which Martin Sheen's character, Kit, describes how he changes his signature each time so that nobody can forge it. However, with Joe there is a more calculated, sinister undercurrent.

Joe also tries to deflect responsibility from his seduction of Ella. He describes 'forces' which push them together and over which he has no control:

'. . . vast gravitational forces which went beyond any 'I' was conscious of, of a complexly woven matrix within which my own conscious decisions were mere threads.'

and

'. . . conscious of the pull that Ella was exerting, almost as though she were hanging heavily and warmly from my skin, a heaviness which centred at the base of my spine and at the back of my thighs . . . '

It is not then surprising for the reader to discover that he describes himself as 'a rootless kind of man' who, through the course of the story, becomes even more adrift:

'I drank from a hipflask . . . It gave me at the same time assurance, certainty, not of anything; confidence simply in the face of the necessity of my isolation.'

He has many connections with other people throughout the novel although none provide him with any way out of his isolation. He is promiscuous but it is a joyless, functionary sex and the landscapes he inhabits are just as grim.

Young Adam is set in an uninviting, dour Scotland. This is a world with no comforts. It is a world of sweat stains, soiled underwear, darts and cigarette butts. It is a weary world where clothes and bedding are repeatedly described as having been 'washed too often' and the narrator himself has not been washed enough:

> 'It occurred to me that I hadn't had a bath for over a week.'

When Leslie has a beer in the pub, Joe describes it as leaving a 'scum-coloured froth round the side of his glass'. The initial comfort that Joe finds in clandestine sex is short-lived and vanishes completely when the secrecy of the liaisons is removed.

Trocchi depicts a Scotland that is particularly unappealing for women (and not just because they meet Joe). Ella has a sexless marriage with her husband and spends her time scrubbing pots and making mince and tatties and cups of tea while wearing sweat-stained dresses that don't fit her anymore. Life outside the barge, in Edinburgh, Glasgow and between, is bleak, rain-soaked and comfortless. While staying in a room and kitchen in Bridgeton in Glasgow, Joe witnesses the dismal life of his landlord's wife, Connie:

'While I was shaving I heard the woman gasp suddenly as the man joined her. He did so with no gentleness, taking what was his.'

Death hangs over the novel. As Joe's affair with Ella builds in intensity, his interest in the case of the body in the canal increases too. Ella joins him in his fascination as he tells us that she 'helped me to cut out all the items from the different papers'. Joe's relationship with Cathie is at one point described as a 'life and death matter', Gwendoline's husband is dead and Joe assumes that the tramp he sees on the canal bank is dead, too.

Trocchi describes a harsh, bitter Scotland in the mid-twentieth century through the disturbed eyes of one of the great anti-heroes of Scottish literature.

The extract

Young Adam

chapter 3

Up on deck the air was cool, cool grey, and over behind the sheds the brick factory-stack was enveloped in a stagnant mushroom of its own yellow smoke. Leslie spat out over the side of the barge and put away his pipe.

'I'll start her up, then,' he said, and went below again.

I let go of the ropes and soon we had moved out into the yellow flank of the river into midstream and were heading for the entrance to the canal. The water was smooth and scum-laden and it seemed to lean against us and fall again, the surface broken with scum-spittles, as we made way. Now and again a piece of pockmarked cork moved past low in the water. There wasn't much traffic on the river. And then, under the dirty lens of sky, Leslie was looking intently towards the quay from which we had just pulled away, marking in his memory, I suppose, the stretch of water from which we had pulled the woman's corpse.

Now, it is boring when you get used to it to crawl along a canal, to wait for a lock to open, for water to level, but you see some interesting things too, like the cyclists on the footpaths where a canal runs through a town, and kids playing, and courting couples. You see a lot of them, especially after dusk, and in the quiet places. They are in the quiet places where there is no footpath and where they have had to climb a fence to get to. Perhaps it is the water that attracts them as much as the seclusion, and of course the danger. In summer they are as thick as midges, and you hear their laughter occasionally towards evening where the broken flowers spread down the bank and touch the water, trailing flowers. You seldom see them: just voices.

Of all the jobs I had been forced to do I think I liked being on the canal best. You are not tied up in one place then as you are if you take a job in town, and sometimes, if you can forget how ludicrously small the distances are, you get the impression that you are travelling. And there is something about travelling.

Soon we were chugging along the banks of the canal and it rolled away behind us like a very neat black tape dividing two masses of green-brown countryside. I could see a boom raised ahead in the distance. It looked very awkward perched there in mid-air like a sign that meant nothing but was black in the thin meagre afternoon light. I was at the wheel, which was aft, and Leslie was sitting on the hatch over the hold, smoking his pipe. He was gazing idly at the landscape, spitting occasionally, lighting and relighting his pipe. Ella was below, tidying up after the meal, and the kid was sitting up at the bows, crosslegged, looking from my point of view like one of those black things you see on telegraph poles. It was a peaceful sight. Leslie looked peaceful too, thinking no doubt how he was going to show off at the dartboard in the little pub at Lairs. I could see him raise a pint of beer to his lips, drink deep, leaving a layer of scum-coloured froth round the side of his glass. He would ask me then if I wanted a game of darts.

Yes, everything was peaceful, like the man who was ploughing in the field far over to the left and like the two cows which were grazing slightly ahead, and there was the fresh air all round me, and everything quiet and a little numb feeling of excitement somewhere deep down in me.

Standing there at the wheel, conscious of the pull Ella was exerting, almost as though she were hanging heavily and warmly from my skin, a heaviness which centred at the base of my spine and at the back of my thighs, and conscious at the same time of the flickering images of the afternoon, it came to me suddenly that touch was more important than sight.

Touch convinced in a way which sight did not. I was struck by the fact that sight is hypnotised by the surfaces of things; more than that, it can know only surfaces, flatnesses at a distance, meagre depths at close range. But the wetness of water felt on the hand and on the wrist is more intimate and more convincing than its colour or even than any flat expanse of sea. The eye, I thought, could never get to the centre of things; there was no intimate connection between my eye and a plant on the windowsill or between my eye and the woman to whom I was about to make love.

And I remembered Cathie, whom I had lived with for two years before I ever came to the barge, and how sometimes I had looked at her and felt appalled by a sense of distance. Say she was sitting on the bed with her knees up, a book in her hands. Somehow, I was not convinced. She was there, but only indirectly, like the wallpaper or the cart drawing up in the street outside the window. I can remember as a small boy I loved touching things, trees, cats, flowers. I saw a violet or a rose but I had to destroy the distance, to feel the soft petals with my fingers, with my cheek; I had to draw the smell of it inside me and feel it living in myself. It was the same with Cathie. I had to go over and bury my head in her thighs – to feel her in my nostrils, to move my hand over her, and finally to draw her whole warm body close to me. But even that was not enough. Even touch was deficient. Perhaps she would be lying naked in my arms. I desired suddenly to see what it was that was so soft and moist and warm. Her body. But that was an abstraction, handy like a price-tag. It had nothing to do with the existence. I drew away from her and scrutinised her, the small breasts with their dull purple tips, the firm brown heap of her belly, and the resilient fleshiness of her thighs. Her buttocks were smooth and yellow, rounded like marble.

But I could not touch these things. I wanted to touch what I saw. But I could only touch a soft thing, a moist thing, a vibrant, clinging thing. Sight and touch may be correlative but their objects are vitally different. Ceasing to see the rise of her breast as I pressed my lips to it to confirm it within myself, the thing which I wished to confirm fled away from me, and in its place was something soft and warm. There was no intimate and necessary relation between what I saw and what I touched. The impressions existed together like a stone and a melody, ludicrous, fraudulent, absurd. It is the feeling that something has eluded you.

I smiled when I thought of it. Cathie. I had met her for the first time in a holiday resort on the west coast. I had gone there because I had to get a job to earn some money. I was leaning on my elbows on the balustrade of the promenade, looking out across the sands towards the sea. I had been aware for some time of a slight movement, of the soft sea wind in coloured cloth, just below me on the beach. A girl was lying there, attempting with modest movements to oil her own back. I don't know whether at that moment she was aware of me. I allowed my eyes to fall occasionally and each time I did so she seemed to react by giving up the attempt to oil her back and by moving her oiled hand over the smooth flesh of her thighs and calves. They were well within her reach and she oiled them with great sensuality.

I watched for perhaps ten minutes. I felt sure by this time that she was inviting me to make contact with her and I was afraid that if I did not do so she would tire, gather her things together, and move along to a more populated part of the beach.

I walked quickly along to the nearest steps, descended to the beach, and walked towards her along the sand. I walked slowly, trying to gauge her reactions.

She was wearing sun-glasses. Behind them, I felt her eyes focused on me, weighing me up.

There is a point at which a man and a woman stalk one another like animals. It is normally in most human situations a very civilised kind of stalking, each move on either side being capable of more than one interpretation. This is a defensive measure. One can, as it were, pretend up to the last moment not to be aware of the sexual construction that can be placed upon one's own movements; one is not bound to admit one's intention to seduce before one is certain that the seduction is consented to. But one can never be quite certain because the other is just as wary, just as unwilling to consent to a man who has not shown clearly his intentions are sexual as the man is to make his intentions obvious without prior consent. So a man and a woman fence with one another and the fencing is the more delicate because neither can wholly trust the other not to simulate ignorance of all that has passed between them. In every situation the man might be a puritan, the woman might wish to have the pleasure of being courted without the finality of the sexual act itself.

Cathie, for example, could have pretended, and, as a matter of fact did pretend, to be surprised at my sudden presence beside her on the beach. It had given her pleasure to be seen stroking her own limbs, but I had no way of knowing whether she would now consent to have me stroke them. She knew this, just as women usually know it, and she was going to enjoy having my purpose unfolded before her. At the point at which she was certain, she would be able to consent or not, and without reference to my desire.

I knew this and she knew it as I sat down beside her and offered her a cigarette. She accepted it. We talked casually about the weather, about the sun, and that made it possible for me to pick up the bottle of sun-tan oil and to examine it. She said I could use some if I wanted to.

I was still fully dressed and I had no bathing costume with me so I said there was not much point in it. Before she could interpret this as a withholding of myself I suggested that I could oil her back for her and I confessed that I had been watching her from the promenade above. She pretended not to know about this, but without a word she rolled over on to her belly and exposed her back to me. She was wearing a two-piece bathing costume of black nylon, the lower part sheathing her buttocks closely and the upper part hidden beneath her except for the thin strand of nylon which ran across her back just below her shoulder-blades.

I began at the small of her back, working with the oil in ever-increasing circles to the limits of her exposed flesh. Soon, however, the massage became a caress, and when I felt her succumb to it, her face buried in her towel in the sand, my fingers slipped first underneath the strap of the top half and then gently on to the smooth mould of her buttocks beneath the taut black nylon. She made no effort to resist. She had shut out the rest of the world from herself, shut out the fear of a casual onlooker from the promenade, by the simple expedient of closing her eyes.

Not far away were some rocks under which I knew it would be possible to be out of sight both from the beach and from the promenade. I did not even know the girl's name at the time and I was wondering whether it would be foolish to suggest going out of sight of other people. After all, even with my hands so intimately at work, she was presently quite safe, all fears gone and tensions relaxed. I could do nothing on the exposed part of the beach. And then, even if she were to consent, the sensations, the looseness which I had already caused in her might fade entirely as we moved to a more private place. She would have a hundred opportunities to revise and decide again. At that moment, had there been no danger of being witnessed, I believe I could have pulled her bathing costume down over her thighs, but whether, out of the sun, after a walk of a hundred yards, I would still be able to assert myself with a girl who was, after all, a complete stranger, I couldn't know. The thought made me pause. I was unwilling to lose what I had already gained in a premature attempt to seduce her. But my doubts didn't remain for long. I felt her abandon. I saw she was totally oblivious to the people who walked past on the promenade overhead. I leaned down close to her and whispered that we could find a place to be alone together farther along the beach.

For a moment she didn't answer. She was lying with her eyes closed, so relaxed that she might have lost consciousness. I sensed then that she wanted to go wherever it was but that she had not yet overcome all her scruples. The longer she analysed, the cooler she would become. Follows, alas, as the night the day. And at such a point it is always difficult to know what to do.

I was a stranger. In the normal way of things there is a structure you have to build up of another person in terms of which that person must make his impact upon you. Beyond this structural idea there is no experience; the structure itself is armour against it. For two people to come close together it is necessary to destroy the structures in terms of which each experiences the other. Cathie had done just that when she accepted a stanger's caress. She could have no means of knowing what she was letting herself in for (unless it was the unknown). Cathie ... that was the name of the girl on the beach. She had thrust away from her the whole system of weights and measures which a conventional upbringing had bequeathed to her. This she did tentatively – her back was towards me and she could at any moment turn, offended – but a tentative movement was all that was necessary. It is necessary only to act 'as if' one's conventional categories were arbitrary for one to come gradually to know that they are, that the profoundest experiences are in the ordinary situation locked out from one's arena of experience by the inflexible barrier of good character.

As a stranger I was afraid of going too fast. As I say, in a situation like this it is always difficult to know what to do. If one is too quick a woman has her 'suspicions' confirmed. She *knows* what you want but is able by some species of rationalization – and in spite of the fact that she knew all along what you wanted, knew, that is, that she had no need of confirmation — to be shocked by your proposal.

'I could do with a walk. Stretch my legs,' she said at last, not looking at me. She got up. She added: 'It's not far, is it?'

Perhaps she too was frightened her desire would be suffocated on the way.

'A hundred yards,' I said, pointing, trying to appear more casual than I was. 'Over by the rocks there.'

Without another word she rose, lifted her towel and the small bag in which she carried her make-up, a book by Daphne du Maurier, and the other articles which a woman takes to the beach, and walked beside me in the direction of the rocks.

We walked separately, without speaking. When we had gone a few yards I took her bag from her and carried it for her. She allowed me to do this, and somehow the action and the consent, the smile, served as words would have.

The rocks were at the far end of the promenade, beyond the last hotel, and they rose up sharply and steeply enough to obscure anything on their seaboard side from the sight of whoever passed by on the promenade. They were shaped like a horse-shoe within which smaller clumps of rock rose upwards from the flat sand, forming tiny water-filled caves. We walked round the nearest point, which sloped down almost to the sea's edge, and as soon as we had done so we had the impression that we were in a kind of amphitheatre.

Once inside, we followed the lee of the outer perimeter to a patch of dry sand, overhung by rock, but which was still in direct line of the sun.

I threw off my jacket, she arranged her towel, and we sat down. The inarticulate closeness which had existed between us a few moments before had evaporated. We were strangers again. She especially seemed suspicious and aloof. We smoked two cigarettes one after the other before she finally lay down and closed her eyes. This time she was lying on her back, the disc of her belly gleaming with oil, her long legs apart and tapering downwards from the sleek casque of her bathing costume. Glistening particles of sand clung to her legs. There was no one in sight.

Cathie. But she was in the past, buried there deeply and finally. Now there was Ella.

But when she came on deck towards evening she didn't even look in my direction. She went forward to where Leslie was sitting and said something which I couldn't catch, and then she came back and I tried to hold her eye, but she avoided my glance and went below.

Her action disturbed me, the more so because I had been watching her and because even as lately as a few moments before when she was standing talking to Leslie the wind had lifted her skirt gently towards the stern and I could imagine what it would have been like if I had been sitting where the kid was and seen her from the other side. I thought then that the skirt would have been clinging up and against her left thigh, like a soft pew-cloth in the wind, and that the muscles of her thigh would have been clearly outlined against the cotton. I found it difficult not to think speculatively about her body, to finger it in my imagination, and yet it had been there at the other side of the partition for two months.

Simultaneously, I derived a pleasing sense of detachment and isolation from the fact that she ignored me. It meant, after all, that she was aware of me, and from that I derived a powerful sense, a vindication of my own existence. To exercise power without exerting it, to be detached and powerful, to be there, silent and indestructible as gods, that is to be a god and why there are gods.

We would see the church tower of Lairs in the distance, a black cone against a red-flecked sky, a witch's hat in a haze of blood. It seemed very far away and enchanted.

Leslie said we would get there before seven. He knew a good place to tie up not far from the little pub he had told me about, so we would have our evening meal and get along to the pub about eight. He wondered whether our discovery of the corpse would be reported in the evening paper. He hoped it would be. Anyway, he would see a paper at the pub. He was in high spirits.

The kid came back from the bows and went down below to his mother. Leslie took over the wheel and I sat down and had a smoke. I was thinking that I didn't want to go to the pub but I didn't see how I could get out of it. I didn't want to play darts, nor to drink for that matter, because Ella wouldn't have drunk anything and she might make that an excuse to refuse me. I had already decided to return earlier than Leslie.

Come to think of it, I had never been alone with Ella, not for more than five minutes at a stretch anyway, and we had hardly spoken. She had resented me from the first, perhaps because I was a man simply and because she judged all men in terms of her experience of Leslie. And of course during the first few weeks Leslie and I had grown quite close to one another. I was, I suppose, his ally against her. But now, after the dangerous intimacy at the cabin table, she must have known I was interested in her. I was anxious now to be alone with her so that I could see what her attitude was.

It was five to seven by Leslie's watch when we made Lairs. We tied up the barge in a little cutting off the main stream and before we went below he pointed out the road we would take to get to the pub afterwards. It was just up round the back of the church, he said, the cosiest little place I had ever seen.

Close up, the church tower looked just as disenchanted as most church towers in Scotland do. Later in the evening, as we skirted the churchyard to reach the pub, I noticed the usual ugly red and black posters proclaiming the evil influence of alcohol and the imminence of the Last Judgement.

'Let's go down and eat,' I said. Leslie followed me. The tea was already on the table, at least mine and his was, because Ella had had hers with the kid, Leslie grunted. He had no suspicions at that time.

It was sausages for tea, and bread and butter and jam

to follow, so, as our sausages were already on the table, there was nothing for her to do except pour the tea. After she had done this, she sat down with her back to me near the stove and went on with her darning.

As I put mustard on my sausages I realized that now I was away from the wheel and the fresh air – the wheel itself under my hands had given me a sense of control –it was only natural that I should have lost that feeling of restrained tension which made me feel so good during the afternoon. It was not so easy down there in the cabin with their double bunk staring me in the face and her with her back turned towards me and Leslie so sure of himself he was thinking only of darts. To Leslie it must have seemed she wasn't thinking of anything. As though she was simply darning his socks, like she might have been shouting at him or scolding the nipper, and wondering how he got such big holes in them. But I knew she couldn't be as calm as she looked. She must have known she had let me go too far at the midday meal to expect me to have forgotten about it. I suspected that that was why she had had her tea early. She had probably thought it over during the afternoon and decided that no good could come of it, perhaps that I was getting ideas above my station, for I had known for a long time that Ella was a snob and she had set her heart on leaving the canal one day to go to live in a 'nice little bungalow', as Leslie called it, in one of the quieter suburbs of Edinburgh. Whatever she was thinking, I decided that it was a good thing I was going to the pub after all, because a couple of whiskies would give me just the right amount of courage.

Leslie finished his food before me because he was anxious to get away to the pub. I have never known a man to hurry his meals so much. He gobbled, always, carrying gobbets of food to his mouth on knife or fork, not alternatively – it depended upon which instrument was nearest which piece of food and upon the shortest distance between plate and mouth. He was leaning forwards now to blow the steam from the surface of his tea.

I looked at Ella's back. It was a broad back, the back of a woman who in maturity was beginning to spread, not slackly, for I could see that her flesh was still firm, but spreading nevertheless, so that a man might feel a powerful lust under him, opaque flesh, strongly muscled, and banded by the strong torque of her body's dynamism.

I intended to return to her, just as soon as possible. I was certain that beneath a few plausible inhibitions she felt as I did, hungry, as though there were a kind of elemental fitness between our respective lusts. I have always felt like that about sex. Each time I close with a woman I have the feeling that we were destined to come together, body to body, just on that way, at that time, in the field or in the bed or wherever it is, and I suppose that doesn't mean anything except that I am always there, waiting, ready to be caught up in it. I am like a sexual divining rod moving furtively at the edges of a meeting. I wait for a sign. It has something to do with the propulsion I feel from the instant desire is born in me, a shadow on a neck, the outline of a thigh, flanks, a gesture of lips wetting themselves, until the instant when

I close with the woman. I resented Ella's present resistance. It was a kind of treason. She had already acquiesced. She could not back out. The whole thing sprang into existence when she stretched up to hang the clothes on the line, when the back of her thighs were bared momentarily up to perhaps six inches below her buttocks. And the risk we would run put an edge to it. I was certain that she was not unaware of my thoughts.

Leslie had already put on his cap and was waiting for me, so I went through into the small for'ard compartment where my bunk was to get mine. When I came back she was telling him not to get drunk. She had her back towards me and I winked at Leslie over her shoulder. Then I walked past her, brushing her buttocks with the back of my hand, and climbed up through the hatch. I felt her shudder. But she didn't say anything.

'See you later,' I said without looking back.

I heard Leslie laugh from above as I climbed through.

about the **author**

Alexander Trocchi

Alexander Trocchi was born in Scotland in 1925 and left the country after excelling at Glasgow University where he studied English and Philosophy. Trocchi left Scotland in his early twenties because, according to John Calder, Trocchi's friend and publisher of much of his work, 'he won a prize that enabled him to write abroad. Scotland was a dull place in the forties and fifties. Trocchi viewed it as parochial, backward and out of date.'

He lived in Paris until the early 1950s and it was during this time that he acquired his lifelong heroin addiction. After some time spent in United States, he settled in London and it was during this time that Calder got to know him:

'In the sixties, everyone was talking about him and his work and he had a huge opinion of himself. When he was on heroin he had big ideas but no energy. After *Young Adam* it was just hack work – he wrote a series of books, one a week. He had a lot of talent but he threw it away.'

Calder has credited Trocchi's resurgence in popularity to Irvine Welsh, who has claimed to be influenced by Trocchi's work. A film adaptation of *Young Adam* by the Recorded Picture Company was filmed in 2002 starring Ewan McGregor with Tilda Swinton, Peter Mullan and Emily Mortimer. It is due for release in 2003.

Alexander Trocchi died in 1984.

selected titles **by**

Alexander Trrocchi

Novels
Young Adam
Sappho of Lesbos
Writers Revolt
Cain's Book

Short stories
New Writers 3

Poetry
Man at Leisure

Erotic novels
Helen and Desire
White Thighs
Frank Harris: My Life and Loves

discussion **points**

1. 'Cosmopolitan scum! A writer of no literary consequence whatsoever.' – Hugh McDiarmid

   Trocchi and McDiarmid had a famous dispute at the Edinburgh Writers Conference of 1962. Do you think this view could be applied to *Young Adam*?

2. Which characters did you find the most compelling? Is it difficult to know them when filtered through such a complex narrator?

3. Do you think Joe is able to convince himself or the reader that he is doing the right thing regarding Daniel Goon? Why do you think he sends the note?

4. There are a large number of women described in the novel, including Ella, her sister, Gwendoline, Cathie, Connie and Mrs Goon. What are Joe's views of women? How do his descriptions connect with his treatment of them? Do you think there is any indication in the narrative that these views were shared by Trocchi?

5. How recognisable is the Scotland described in *Young Adam*? Is this a country you recognise from other fiction?

6. How would you explain Joe's lack of interest in Ella's son, Jim?

press **quotes**

'With overtones of Albert Camus' *The Outsider*, this is a darkly atmospheric story of an anti-hero, stumbling through an existentialist world filled with themes of sex and murder. Compelling.'
– *Buzz*

'This sordid story of murder and seduction on a barge between Glasgow and Edinburgh contains exceptionally fine writing, evoking a dank, stifling underworld of confused and errant motives.'
– *The Times*

'Trocchi writes extremely well, in a hip and eerily affectless tone that confirms earlier critics' detection of a strong flavour of Albert Camus' *The Outsider*.'
– *Herald*

'Alexander Trocchi may be the greatest unknown writer in the world … what Trocchi was about, in life and art, was the testing of boundaries, the eradication of acceptable behaviour in the name of something more engaged.' – *Bloomsbury Review*

'A very fine writer.'
– Norman Mailer

'Everyone should read *Young Adam*.'
– *Times Literary Supplement*

similar **reads**

The Outsider by Albert Camus
(Penguin Books; ISBN: 0141182504)
Young Adam has been described as Trocchi's *The Outsider*. Camus' classic existentialist novel of 1942 describes the experience of a young man, Meursault, who, through his involvement in a murder, 'dies for the truth'.

A Hero of Our Time by Mikhail Lermontov
(Penguin Books; ISBN: 0140447954)
First published in Russia in 1840, *A Hero of Our Time* describes five episodes in the life of Pechorin, told through the eyes of those who met him and through a discovered diary. Like Joe in *Young Adam*, Pechorin's constant struggles against boredom lead to destruction and death.

Marabou Stork Nightmares by Irvine Welsh
(Vintage; ISBN: 009943511X)
Irvine Welsh's second novel describes the life of a young man through three narrative strands. As the story unfolds it becomes clear a violent crime has

been committed and the young man knows much more than he has revealed.

Under the Skin by Michel Faber
(*Canongate Books Ltd; ISBN: 1841950947*)
Michel Faber's unusual and disturbing story is told through the eyes of the alienated Isserley as she picks up hitchhikers on the A9. Isserley is an outsider with an unexpected secret.

The Private Memoirs and Confessions of a Justified Sinner by James Hogg
(*Canongate Books Ltd; ISBN: 0862413400*)
Robert is a devout young man who uses the Calvinist doctrine of predestination to justify his murderous ambition. A masterpiece of Scottish fiction.

Cain's Book by Alexander Trocchi
(*Calder Publications Ltd; ISBN: 0714542334*)
Joe Necchi is a junkie living on a barge in New York. *Cain's Book* was a hugely controversial novel when it was published in the UK in the sixties and was the subject of an obscenity trial in Sheffield.

competition

Your chance to win ten contemporary works of fiction signed by their authors.

The *Read Around Books* series was developed by Scottish Book Trust to encourage readers to widen their reading interests and discover writers they had never tried before. Has it been a success? We want to hear from you. Tell us if you have enjoyed this little series or not and if you did, do you have any suggestions for authors who should be included in the series in the future.

Writer to us now with the following information:

Name and address
Email address
Are you a member of a readers' group?
Name of readers' group

Send us the information above and we will enter you into our prize draw to be drawn on 22 August 2003.

Send to:
RAB Draw
Scottish Book Trust
137 Dundee Street
Edinburgh EH11 1BG

scottish **book trust**

What is Scottish Book Trust?

Scottish Book Trust exists to serve readers and writers in Scotland. We work to ensure that everyone has access to good books, and to related resources and opportunities.

We do this in a number of ways:

- By operating the Writers in Scotland Scheme, which funds over 1,400 visits a year by Scottish writers to a variety of institutions and groups
- By supporting Scottish writing through a programme of professional training opportunities for writers
- By publishing a wide variety of resources and leaflets to support readership
- By promoting initiatives such as National Poetry Day and World Book Day
- And through our Book Information Service, providing free advice and support to readers and writers, and the general public.

For more information please visit
www.scottishbooktrust.com

titles **in the series**

Available in the Read Around Books series

Iain Crichton Smith's *Murdo: The Life and Works,*
  by Douglas Gifford

Meaghan Delahunt's *In The Blue House,*
  by Gavin Wallace

Michel Faber's *Under the Skin,* by Mary Firth

Jonathan Falla's *Blue Poppies,* by Rosemary Goring

Janice Galloway's *Clara,* by David Robinson

Andrew Greig's *That Summer,* by Alan Taylor

Anne MacLeod's *The Dark Ship,* by Lindsey Fraser

Maggie O'Farrell's *After You'd Gone,* by Rosemary Goring

Suhayl Saadi's *The Burning Mirror,*
  by Catherine McInerney

Ali Smith's *Hotel World,* by Kathryn Ross

Muriel Spark's *The Comforters,* by Alan Taylor

Alexander Trocchi's *Young Adam,* by Gillian Mackay